Copyright © **ticktock** Entertainment Ltd 2004

First published in Great Britain in 2004 by **ticktock** Media Ltd.,
Unit 2, Orchard Business Centre, North Farm Road, Tunbridge Wells, Kent, TN2 3XF

We would like to thank: Meme Ltd.

Picture Credits: Saab Scania 4. Dave Arnold/copcar.com 5, 9. US Coastguard 6, 7 & 8.
Portland Mountain Rescue Unit 9, 15, 16 & 17.

Every effort has been made to trace the copyright holders, and we apologise in advance for any unintentional omissions.
We would be pleased to insert the appropriate acknowledgements in any subsequent edition of this publication.

ISBN 1 86007 445 6 HB
ISBN 1 86007 441 3 PB

Printed in China

Contents

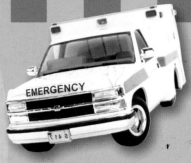

Learning Advice

This book is designed to be both stimulating and accessible to young readers. Young children can show a wide range in ability. This is not necessarily a guide to later levels of achievement. Young children learn well through sharing. Therefore, this book should be treated as an opportunity to share and talk about what is on each page. At this age, all reading should be shared reading. By showing a child that you find reading exciting, you will pass this positive image on to your child. Try to involve your child in each story as much as possible, ask and answer questions and talk about any ideas that arise. Encourage your child to come up with ideas on his or her own. Many books on rescue vehicles are available at your local library.

Rescue Vehicles
Fire, Police and Ambulance

Rescue vehicles help us in emergencies.
They often have to go very fast. They have lights and sirens so you can hear when they are coming.

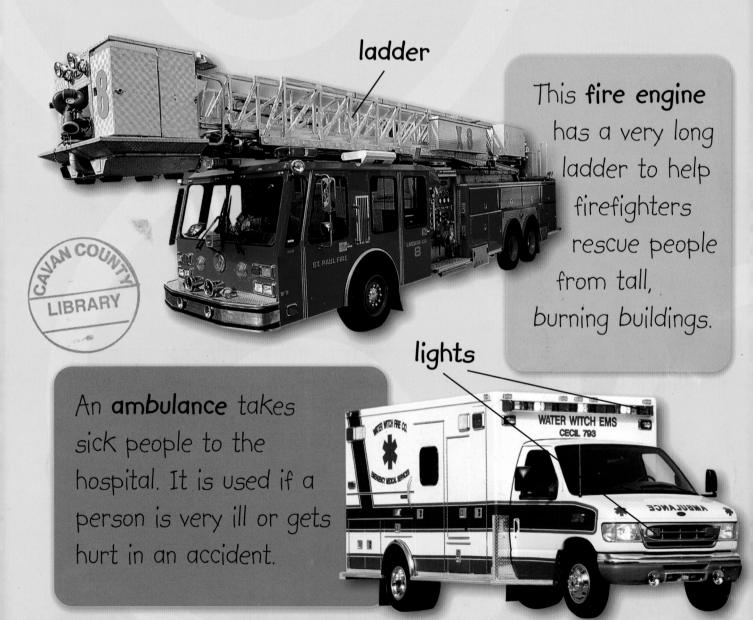

ladder

This **fire engine** has a very long ladder to help firefighters rescue people from tall, burning buildings.

ST. PAUL FIRE

LADDER CO. 8

lights

An **ambulance** takes sick people to the hospital. It is used if a person is very ill or gets hurt in an accident.

WATER WITCH FIRE CO.

EMERGENCY MEDICAL SERVICES

WATER WITCH EMS
CECIL 793

AMBULANCE

This is a **police car**. It is painted with bright colours so that people can see it easily when it speeds past.

seat

A **police motorcycle** is very useful. It allows police officers to zip up and down motorways and through busy city streets.

Rescue Words

Can you find these words on the page?

fire engine

ambulance

lights

police car

seat

police motorcycle

ladder

Rescue Vehicles:
Air and Sea

Sometimes rescue vehicles need to go where there are no roads. The people who use rescue vehicles often have to be very brave.

A **rescue helicopter** can fly low over the sea or mountains. It can land where there are no runways. It can hover while a member of the crew throws down a rope to a stranded person.

cabin

jet spray

A **fireboat** fights fires at sea. These boats put out fires by using sea water that shoots out from the boat in a high jet spray.

wings

This airtanker fights forest fires by dropping special powder on the blaze to try to stop it from spreading further.

Sometimes when people are lost at sea, the coastguard sends a **coastguard boat** to rescue them.

Rescue Words

Can you find these words on the page?

rescue helicopter

airtanker

wings

fireboat

cabin

coastguard boat

jet spray

Word Puzzles

Look at these rescue pictures.
Can you tell what order the words should go in?

1

very   noisy   The   is   helicopter

Rescue Vehicles Words

1

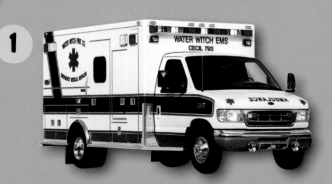

Can you remember what these rescue vehicles are called?

2

fire engine

The

yellow

is

white

The

snow

is

3

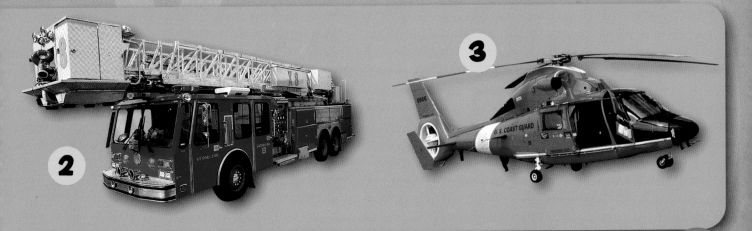

2

3

Word Puzzles answers: 1. The helicopter is very noisy. **2.** The fire engine is yellow. **3.** The snow is white.

A Story to Read:
Ron to the Rescue

Ron, the brave **firefighter**, loves to put out fires. His shiny, red fire engine has big, black tyres.

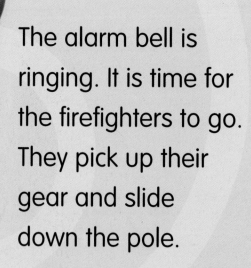

The alarm bell is ringing. It is time for the firefighters to go. They pick up their gear and slide down the pole.

The **fire engine** goes very fast. Everybody moves aside as the truck picks up speed.

Wheeeeeee! The siren is very loud. Ron looks into the sky for signs of smoke clouds.

The fire engine stops. Ron can see the smoke! It is coming from a garden.

Ron puts on his breathing mask. Next, he unwinds the fire hose and runs up the path.

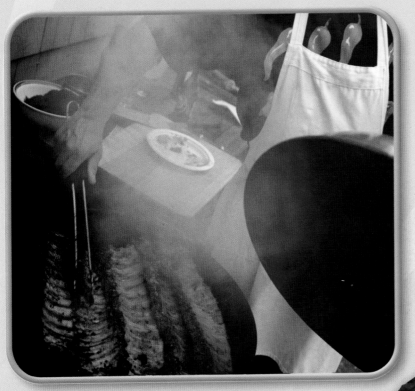

Ron rushes to the garden, but the smoke is getting thinner. It is coming from a **barbecue**. A man is cooking dinner!

The man gives Ron a burger.
Ron walks back to his truck.
At least there was no fire.
What a stroke of luck!

Can you answer these questions about the story you have just read?

1 What is Ron's job?
2 How does Ron get to the fire?
3 Where is the smoke coming from?

A Story to Share:
Snow Mountain Rescue

Can you say the words in **bold**? Use the pictures to help you.

Today, Rebecca is going skiing in the snow. Have fun, Rebecca, but be careful!

The weather is bad and Rebecca gets lost! Which rescue vehicle can help her?

The **ambulance** can help if Rebecca is hurt, but it can't drive in the snow! No, the ambulance can't help.

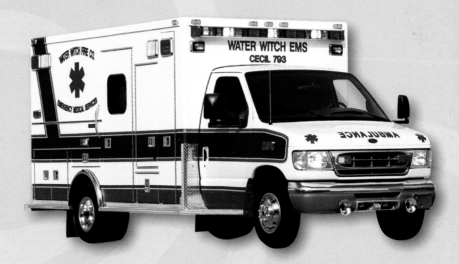

The **fire engine** could reach up high with its long ladder. But it can't drive up the mountain! No, the fire engine can't help.

The **police motorcycle** is speedy enough to drive up the mountain, but Rebecca won't be able to ride on it if she is hurt. No, the police motorcycle can't help!

The **rescue helicopter** can fly over mountains, and it can land on the snow. Can the helicopter rescue Rebecca?

Yes! The rescue helicopter can see Rebecca. The pilot lands nearby. Rebecca is not hurt. She is just very cold. She is happy to get inside the warm helicopter.

Rebecca will never go skiing by herself again. Have fun, Rebecca! Keep safe!

Ambulance Rescue Game

Which will be the first ambulance to deliver a patient to the hospital?

Race to the rescue in this exciting game for 2 to 4 players!

First, find a small plastic toy for each player. Place each toy on the start line. Then, roll a dice to see who goes first.

Each player takes it in turn to move along the road. Follow the road-side instructions along the way. The first person to reach the hospital wins!

START

9

10
Take a lady home after her operation. Move forward 2 spaces.

FINISH
Hooray! You got to the hospital in time. You win!

18

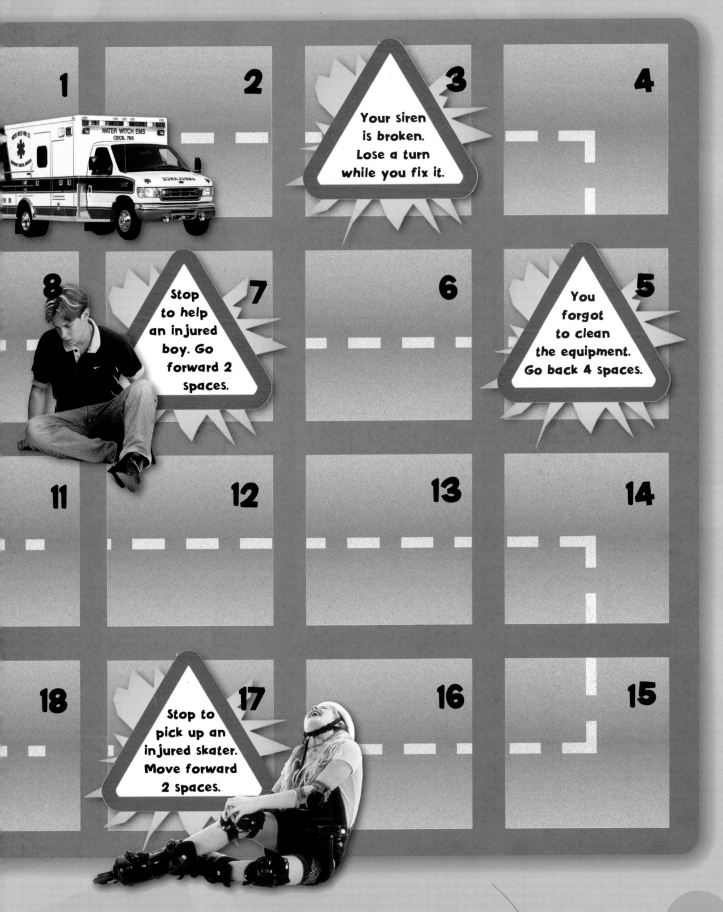

A Bedtime Story:
Baby Emergency

Rachael and her mother are driving to the supermarket to do the weekly shopping. Rachael likes to go shopping with her mum, because she likes to help.

Rachael will soon have a new baby sister, so her mum needs a helper around.

The supermarket is hard work. Rachael helps as much as she can. She helps to push the trolley and then lifts some of the shopping bags into the car.

It is very busy and Rachael's mum is soon very tired. By the time Rachael has finished packing the car with shopping, her mother is not feeling well at all.

On the way home, the traffic is very bad. Their car is stuck in a big jam. Then, Rachael's mother stops the car.

"I think that your little sister is going to be born a bit early," she gasps. "We need to go to the hospital."

Rachael is scared. The traffic is not moving. Her mother gets out her mobile phone. She dials the emergency services and tells the operator what is happening.

"Hold on," says the operator. "We are sending an ambulance to help you."

Rachael can tell that her mother is in pain so she does her best to help keep her calm. "Don't worry," Rachael says, "the ambulance will not get stuck in the traffic, it has lights and a siren."

It is not long before Rachael can hear the sound of the ambulance coming nearer. Soon, there it is, making its way through the traffic. The ambulance crew jump out and run to Rachael's mum.

"It's too far to go to the hospital," the driver says to Rachael. "Your mother will need to have the baby in the ambulance. Don't worry, it will be quite safe. We have all the equipment we need right here."

Rachael is not allowed in the ambulance with her mum, but before long the driver comes back looking very pleased.

"Congratulations!" he says, "You have a brand-new baby sister."
"You can ride with us back to the hospital", the ambulance driver says to Rachael.

"Can you turn on the lights and siren while we drive?" asks Rachael. The ambulance driver laughs. "What?" he says, "And wake up your little sister?" Rachael looks into the back of the ambulance. Her new little sister is already fast asleep!

Rescue Counting:
Emergency Numbers

How many rescue vehicles are there in each line?

Can you count them?

Which line has the most rescue vehicles in it?

Which line has the least?

Number words

One
Two
Three
Four
Five
Six

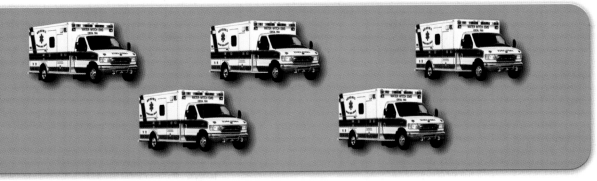

Can you match the number words to the right number of rescue vehicles? Use the colour codes to help you.

Rescue Counting:
Race to the Rescue

Look at these two fire engines.

They are both the same, but they have a different number of fires to put out. Which one will finish first?

How many fires does fire engine 1 have to put out?

How many fires does fire engine 2 have to put out?

Do you know which rescue vehicle can help?

Use the colour clues to help you.

How many injured skaters does the ambulance have to pick up?

How many boaters does the coastguard boat have to rescue?

Spot the Difference

Rescuers need to be very aware. They have to be able to spot danger and work out the best way to rescue someone.

Look at these two pictures.
Can you spot the four differences between them?

Make a Firefighter's Badge

Every firefighter has a badge. Follow these step-by-step instructions to make your own. Ask an adult to help you.

You will need: 1. scissors (and an adult to use them) 2. a piece of card 3. colouring pens or pencils 4. sticky tape

1. Take a square piece of card as big as you would like your badge to be.

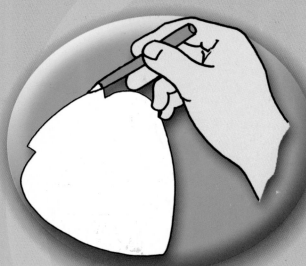

2. Draw a badge shape like the one shown here.

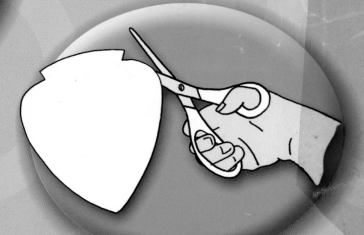

3. Cut out the badge. Get an adult to help you with the scissors.

4. Look at this picture of a firefighter's badge. Try to copy the details onto your badge.

5. Colour your badge in using colouring pens or pencils.

6. Stick your badge to your coat or jumper with sticky tape. Imagine you have been called out to a fire. What things will you need to put the fire out?

IMPORTANT FIREFIGHTING RULES

1. Never try to put out a fire by yourself.

2. Run to the nearest adult and tell them where the fire is.

3. If no adult is nearby, leave the fire and call out until an adult hears.

4. Never ever return to a fire.

5. If the fire is indoors, leave the building straight away.

6. Try to warn other people in the building about the fire, but do not stay in the building.

Word Finder

Here are some of the words used in this book. Can you remember what they mean? Go back and look through the book to see if you can find each word again.

fire engine	firefighter	hose
police car	ambulance	barbecue
helicopter	rescue	fireboat
badge	siren	airtanker
wings	lights	cabin
seat	help	jet spray
ladder	snow	smoke